OXFORD BOOKW
Human I

The Summer Intern

HELEN SALTER

Stage 2 (700 headwords)

Illustrated by Nathalie Dion

Series Editor: Rachel Bladon
Founder Editors: Jennifer Bassett
and Tricia Hedge

OXFORD
UNIVERSITY PRESS

Great Clarendon Street, Oxford, OX2 6DP, United Kingdom

Oxford University Press is a department of the University of Oxford.
It furthers the University's objective of excellence in research, scholarship,
and education by publishing worldwide. Oxford is a registered trade
mark of Oxford University Press in the UK and in certain other countries

© Oxford University Press 2016

The moral rights of the author have been asserted

First published in Oxford Bookworms 2016

10 9 8 7 6 5 4 3 2 1

No unauthorized photocopying

All rights reserved. No part of this publication may be reproduced,
stored in a retrieval system, or transmitted, in any form or by any means,
without the prior permission in writing of Oxford University Press, or as
expressly permitted by law, by licence or under terms agreed with the
appropriate reprographics rights organization. Enquiries concerning
reproduction outside the scope of the above should be sent to the ELT
Rights Department, Oxford University Press, at the address above

You must not circulate this work in any other form and you must
impose this same condition on any acquirer

Links to third party websites are provided by Oxford in good faith and
for information only. Oxford disclaims any responsibility for the materials
contained in any third party website referenced in this work

ISBN: 978 0 19 423803 8 Book

A complete recording of this Bookworms edition of *The Summer Intern* is available.

Printed in China

Word count (main text): 6,762

For more information on the Oxford Bookworms Library,
visit www.oup.com/elt/gradedreaders

ACKNOWLEDGEMENTS

Cover photographs reproduced with permission from: Shutterstock (teen girl/Stock-Asso),
(magazine pieces/Trinet Uzun).

The Publisher would like to thank the following for permissions to reproduce photographs:
123RF (emoticons/annaleni)

Illustrations by: Nathalie Dion/Anna Goodson Illustration Agency

CONTENTS

Chapter 1
Gloss

Anna walked through the door of the *Gloss* office, feeling excited. She had an internship there for a month this summer. Most of her friends were working in shops or for boring businesses, but Anna was at *Gloss*, a new website for teenagers! *Gloss* had everything: if you wanted to read about beauty, fashion, or famous people, you looked on the *Gloss* website.

When Anna walked into the office, everyone was already busy around her, writing or talking on the phone. For her first job of the day, she had to get the mail – and this morning, as usual, there were lots of parcels. Every day, *Gloss* got lots of exciting things in the mail: make-up, dresses, bags, shoes… The people who made these things sent them because they wanted the *Gloss* writers to tell teenagers about them on the website.

Today, there were lots of parcels for Tina. Tina was the website's Editor: she decided what to post on the website each week, and she wrote the *Gloss* blog. Anna thought that Tina had a great job – she was always going to parties and meeting famous people!

Tina was not in her office when Anna went in, and Anna was pleased. She was a little afraid of Tina because she always said what she thought and she quickly got angry about things.

Next, Anna took three big parcels to Stella's desk. Stella was *Gloss*'s Fashion and Beauty Writer, so she wrote all the features for the website. She was on the phone when Anna brought the parcels to her, and she did not look up when she took them. Stella was very hard-working, and it was not always easy to talk to her.

Anna took three big parcels to Stella's desk.

Last, there was a parcel for Ruby, the *Gloss* Photographer. Ruby's job was to take some of the photos for the website, find other pictures and videos, and make *Gloss*'s vlogs. Anna always liked talking to her, and hearing about her fashion and beauty shoots.

'My new camera!' Ruby said happily, taking the parcel. She pushed lots of paper and empty coffee cups to one side of her desk to make room. 'Thanks, Anna.'

Ruby was the untidiest person in the office, but she was also the friendliest. She was always singing and laughing.

Anna was starting to ask Ruby about the new camera when her phone rang. She took it out of her pocket; it was her mum.

'Hello, Mum,' she said, turning away and speaking quietly. 'I forgot to turn my phone off. I'm at work.'

'How are you?' said her mum. 'Are you OK?'

'I'm fine. But, Mum, I can't talk now.'

'OK, then. Have a good day, and call me when you're on the train. Oh, and Anna, don't forget to eat all your lunch, will you?'

Anna's mum always wanted her to eat more.

'OK, Mum,' replied Anna.

'Ooh, did I tell you who was in the shop yesterday?' her mum started to say.

'Mum,' said Anna quickly, 'can you tell me later? I can't talk while I'm at work.'

Anna tried not to sound angry. Her mum always wanted to know that she was OK – but she was fifteen, not five!

Anna said goodbye to her mum, and turned her phone off. A second later, the door of the office opened, and Tina walked in, calling loudly, 'Meeting, everybody. Now!'

Anna went into the meeting room, and looked nervously around the table at Tina, Stella, and Ruby. This meeting was important for her. She was happy to be at *Gloss*, but she didn't want just to make the coffee and get the mail for the next month. She loved writing, and she really wanted to try to write a feature for the website.

I'll say something to Tina today, at this meeting, she thought. I'll say that I'd like to write something.

'Ideas!' said Tina, and she looked around the table. 'I want good ideas! We are getting lots of hits now, but we need more. So what features can we post this week? Stella, you first!'

Stella looked down at her notebook with a worried look on her face. 'Teenagers wear lots of black and grey,' she said. 'Let's write a feature about wearing more colour.'

'That's nothing new,' said Tina. 'Any other ideas?'

'I'm thinking... a vlog about street fashion,' said Ruby. 'We film people in the street and they tell us what they like to wear, and why.'

'Ideas!' said Tina. 'I want good ideas!'

'No,' said Tina. 'I want something stronger than that.'

Anna knew that she had to say something. She wanted Tina to know that she had ideas, too.

'Tina?' she said, in a very small voice.

Tina turned to Anna, and Anna felt everyone's eyes on her. Her face went red, and she tried not to sound afraid.

'Er, I thought that something about social media would be interesting?'

'For example?' said Tina.

'Well... when we're online, we tell people about our lives. But do we say too much?'

Anna waited. Is Tina going to say yes to an idea from me, the girl who gets the mail?

'No,' Tina said. '*Teen Talks* did that last month. We don't take ideas from other websites. None of you have any good ideas, then! Nothing new!'

She stood and left the room.

'I didn't know that *Teen Talks* just did that fo Anna said to Ruby when they walked back to thei

'Don't worry,' said Ruby. 'You've got ideas, an good. Do you want to be a writer?'

'I do!' said Anna. She was always writing – an people said that she was very good at it. 'I reall to try and write something while I'm here. Bu doesn't like her interns to write features; she just wants them to make coffee and get the mail.'

'Do you want to be a writer?'

Ruby smiled. 'Talk to her about it another day,' she said. 'She isn't very happy today because she's interviewing Jamie Fenton on Friday.'

'Jamie Fenton?' said Anna. Jamie was a singer with the group High Five. Her best friend Katie loved them!

Ruby laughed. 'Yes, but it isn't easy to write about him. He left one interview because he didn't like the questions.'

Anna laughed, but she sat down heavily at her desk. Will Tina ever like my ideas? she thought. This is important to me. I want this internship to go well! I lost my best friend for this job!

Chapter 2
Katie

Every time Anna thought about her best friend Katie, she felt upset.

It all went wrong with Katie when Anna got the job at *Gloss*. Anna and Katie were great friends and they did everything together, but they were very different. Anna loved books and writing; and Katie loved beauty and fashion.

Because of this, they both wanted to do the internship at *Gloss*. So when Anna got the job, she was very happy, but she felt bad for Katie, too, and she was afraid to tell her. She did not say anything at first. Then her mum told Carla's mum, who told Carla, who told Katie.

Anna sent Katie a message, but it was too late and Katie replied:

> Why didn't you tell me about the Gloss job yourself? 😮

Anna tried to explain, but Katie did not answer. Then, one of their friends, Carla, posted on social media:

> Just heard that you didn't get the Gloss job, Katie – can't believe it! You know SO much about famous people and beauty. But I also heard that you've got a job at Scarf Shop. Me too!

Soon, Katie was sitting next to Carla in all their lessons – and still not replying to Anna's messages.

Anna thought about this every day, and the morning after the ideas meeting, when she got on the train, she decided to message Katie again. She took her phone out of her bag, but then it started to ring.

Katie? No. It was her mum.

Soon, Katie was sitting next to Carla in all their lessons.

'I was thinking, shall I come to *Gloss* and meet you today?' her mum said.

Anna thought about it. Her mum in the *Gloss* office? No. That was not a good idea.

'I'm OK, Mum, really,' said Anna. 'You don't have to worry.'

'Have you heard anything from Katie?' said her mum.

'No,' said Anna. 'Look, sorry, Mum, but I have to go; I'm getting off the train in a minute. I'll see you later.'

Anna started to make some notes about ideas for features:

A feature about what to do when…
- your mum worries about you too much
- your best friend stops speaking to you

Is everyone's life like this? thought Anna. Or is it just me?

Chapter 3
Jamie Fenton

When Anna arrived in the office, Tina was out and Ruby was playing High Five songs loudly.

Anna made coffee for everyone, and then she went into the fashion room. Tina, Stella, and Ruby kept all the things sent by fashion and beauty companies here – clothes, bags, shoes, and make-up. Stella wanted Anna to tidy it, because no one could find anything in there. So she put the bags in one place, the dresses in another, and all the shoes in boxes. After a few hours, the fashion room was starting to look better.

'This is nice!' said a voice. 'Stella will love it – she's *so* tidy.'

Anna turned and saw Ruby by the door. 'Do you want to come to lunch with me and Stella?' asked Ruby.

Anna smiled. It was nice of Ruby to ask her.

'Thanks,' she answered. 'But I already have some lunch. I brought it in.'

She did not say that she did not have any money to go out for lunch because *Gloss* did not pay interns!

Anna's phone beeped, and she looked at it quickly. 'My mum,' she said to Ruby. 'She messages me all the time!'

Ruby laughed, said goodbye, and left, and then the office went quiet. Anna finished tidying the clothes, and then went and looked out of the window of the empty office. She was trying to find her lunch in her bag when she heard a voice behind her.

'Is this the *Gloss* office?'

Anna turned and nearly dropped her bag.

It was a boy. But not just any boy: it was Jamie Fenton… Jamie Fenton from High Five!

It was Jamie Fenton from High Five!

He's short, Anna thought to herself. Shorter than he looks on TV!

'Hi,' he said. 'I'm Jamie.'

'Er, I know,' said Anna. Her voice sounded strange. 'I'm Anna. Er, I'm very sorry, but I thought that the interview was tomorrow?'

Jamie looked at his phone, then at Anna. 'Well, I'm here now. I can't come back tomorrow.'

Help! thought Anna. What now? Everyone said that he was difficult, and now he was here, a day early, and there was no one to help! When he hears that Tina isn't here, he'll leave, she thought. Tina will be so angry!

'Please have a seat,' said Anna nervously. She pulled out Ruby's chair for Jamie. 'I'll phone the Editor right now.'

Anna's hands were shaking. She called Tina's number. Answer! Answer! she thought. What will I do if she doesn't answer?

Talk to him yourself! said a little voice inside Anna's head. It will be a great feature: 'Fifteen-year-old interviews Jamie Fenton!'

Another little voice inside her head said that was not a good idea.

'Hello?' said Tina at last. It sounded like she was in a shop.

'Hi, Tina!' said Anna. 'It's Anna here. I'm really sorry, but there's a problem. It's Jamie Fenton. He's here in the office, now!'

'What?' said Tina. 'Today's Thursday. He's coming tomorrow!'

Anna looked at Jamie. Oh dear: he was looking at all the empty coffee cups and untidy papers on Ruby's desk.

Anna turned and said in a quiet voice, 'Yes, but he got the day wrong. He's here now.'

Tina was silent for a second or two, then she said, 'OK. I'm coming now!'

Anna put down the phone. 'The Editor's coming,' she said. And at that second, they heard someone on the stairs outside.

Jamie looked at the door. 'That was quick!'

But it wasn't Tina. It was Anna's mum!

'Mum! What are you doing here?' she said.

Her mum was wearing a brown coat and holding an old bag. She did not look right in the *Gloss* office.

'Is that how you say hello to your mother?' said her mum. 'You forgot your lunch.' She turned to Jamie Fenton and said, 'She forgets everything.'

Oh no! thought Anna. My mum doesn't know who Jamie Fenton is!

'Thanks, Mum,' said Anna. She quickly took the lunch from her mum and smiled nervously. OK, Mum, you can go now, she thought to herself.

'Where is everybody?' said her mum.

'They've gone to lunch,' replied Anna. 'But they'll be back soon.'

'These are nice offices, aren't they?' her mum said to Jamie. 'Do you work here?'

'No,' said Jamie. 'I'm a singer.'

*Oh no! thought Anna. My mum doesn't know
who Jamie Fenton is!*

Her mum smiled at Jamie. 'Well, don't worry,' she said. 'It's hard to get a real job these days. And you're only young. There's lots of food in that bag, if you're hungry.'

Jamie gave Anna's mum a strange look, but there was a little smile on his face, too. Help!

'Thank you, Mum!' Anna said quickly. 'I'll see you later.'

'Well, I can stay and have lunch with you, if you like,' said her mum.

'Thanks, Mum, but Jamie's here for an interview, and the Editor will be here in a minute,' said Anna. She took her mum's arm and went with her to the door. 'I'll see you later.'

'OK, see you later, then,' said her mum, but before she shut the door behind her, she put her head around it and called, 'Don't forget to eat your lunch!'

Anna looked at Jamie Fenton's face. What is he thinking now? she thought to herself.

She was very surprised when he laughed.

'Your mum's great,' he said. 'You're lucky. I'm away with High Five for six months every year. I don't see my mum much.'

Anna couldn't believe it: was Jamie Fenton really saying that he missed his mum?

'And I get so bored of hotel food,' Jamie went on. 'I miss my mum's home cooking.'

'Well, I've got some of my mum's home-made cookies here,' said Anna. 'Would you like one?'

'Oh yes, please,' said Jamie. 'I didn't have any breakfast.'

'Don't tell my mum that,' Anna laughed.

So they sat and ate cookies, and talked about their mums and about their favourite home-made food. It was like eating lunch with a friend from school, but every few seconds, Anna remembered that this was Jamie Fenton!

'So what do you do here, Anna?' asked Jamie.

Anna started to answer, but the door of the office opened and Tina walked in. Stella and Ruby were behind her.

'Jamie!' said Tina warmly, and she hurried him into her office.

Ruby looked at Anna and her mouth fell open. 'Wow! Tell us everything!'

'He talked about his mum's cooking!' said Anna. 'And he ate half of my mum's cookies!'

'I can't believe it,' Ruby told Stella. 'Every week, I say that I will bring in lunch, and I never do.'

Anna sat back in her chair. I had lunch with Jamie Fenton, she thought. And he was nice!

'What shall I do for you this afternoon?' she asked Stella. I sat talking to Jamie Fenton! she thought to herself. Give me something exciting! Something new!

'Have you tidied the make-up yet?' said Stella.

Chapter 4
No More Secrets

'Tina's really happy today!' Stella said to Ruby. They were in the office kitchen with Anna.

'I know,' said Ruby. 'She was smiling! In the morning! Let's look at her blog and find out why.' She took her phone out of her pocket, opened the *Gloss* website, and found the Editor's blog.

'Look!' she said, and showed Stella and Anna her phone. Tina's piece in her blog that morning said:

> Great interview with Jamie Fenton yesterday. Read all about it on *Gloss* this afternoon!

Tina came into the kitchen, and Ruby quickly put her phone back in her pocket.

'How did the interview go, Tina?' said Stella.

'It was good!' said Tina. 'Usually famous people don't want to tell you anything about their lives. But he was really nice, and really happy to talk!'

'That's because of Anna!' said Ruby excitedly. 'Anna talked to him about his mum!'

'Really?' said Tina, looking at Anna.

'She gave him home-made cookies,' said Ruby. 'Anyone will talk after a cookie or two!'

'*How did the interview go, Tina?*'

Anna smiled.

'Well, thanks, Anna,' said Tina. She took her cup of coffee and started walking out of the kitchen, but then turned back. 'What are you doing today?'

'I have to finish tidying the make-up,' said Anna.

'And what would you like to do after that?' said Tina.

Ruby looked at Anna. 'Go on!' she said quietly.

'Er... well, I'd really like to write something, if that's OK,' said Anna. 'I love writing. It's why I wanted to come and work here.'

Tina thought for a second. 'I remember that your school said that you could write well,' she said. 'Usually I don't like interns to do any writing, but you can have a try. You can help Stella with her feature about autumn fashion.'

Wow, was this really happening?

'Thank you,' said Anna.

'Do a good job, OK?' said Tina.

＊ ＊ ＊

There was a message on Anna's phone from her mum when she got on the train that afternoon:

How was your day?

Anna messaged back:

GREAT! 😊

A few seconds later, her phone rang.

'That sounds good!' said her mum.

'It was!' laughed Anna. 'I worked on my first feature. Stella, the Features Writer, helped me, but I wrote most of it. She put my name on it. Oh, and Mum, there's a photo on the website of me, Ruby, and Stella with Jamie Fenton – you know, the singer who came to the office yesterday?'

'That's great!' said her mum.

'I'll tell you all about it when I get home,' Anna said. 'See you soon.'

Anna was still thinking about her day when she got off the train, so at first she did not see Katie, who was walking in front of her. But then she saw the Scarf Shop shirt and the long dark hair.

'Katie!' she called.

Katie turned. She did not smile, but she stopped walking.

'Hi!' said Anna.

'Hi,' said Katie.

'How's Scarf Shop?' Anna asked.

'It's boring,' said Katie. 'I put scarves in bags. I tidy scarves. When I shut my eyes, I see scarves. How's *Gloss*?'

Anna wanted to tell Katie about her feature and about meeting Jamie Fenton. But now was not the right time. She did not want Katie to feel jealous, so she said, 'A lot of the time at *Gloss*, I tidy clothes and make-up – and

make coffee for everyone. Sometimes it's really boring –
and they're not even paying me!'

Was Katie's face softening a little?

'It's really nice to see you,' said Anna. 'I've missed
you.'

Was Katie's face softening a little?

'I've missed you too,' said Katie. 'I was upset because you didn't tell me about the job at *Gloss*. I didn't want to hear something like that from Carla.'

'I'm really sorry,' said Anna. 'I wanted to say something about the job, but I felt bad about it, and I didn't know how to tell you.'

Katie smiled at Anna. 'Well, next time, tell me first, OK? No more secrets.'

Do I say something now about Jamie Fenton? thought Anna. But they were nearly at the end of Katie's street, and Katie looked at her watch. 'Listen, Anna, I have to go now, but I'll message you later. Do you want to come to my house one evening this week? Tomorrow, perhaps, after you finish work?'

'Yes, sure,' said Anna. They said goodbye, and Anna walked home. She felt much better, but she was worried, too. How am I going to explain that I had lunch with Katie's favourite singer? Anna thought. And how is she going to feel about that?

But she did not need to tell Katie. Half an hour later, she got a message from her:

> Really boring at Gloss, is it? Why didn't you tell me about this? 😦

Below was the photo of Anna with Jamie Fenton.

Oh no, thought Anna. Katie's never going to want to be my friend again now.

Chapter 5
Comments

All weekend, Katie did not reply to Anna's messages, and when Anna went to her house, there was no answer.

I am so stupid, Anna thought. Why didn't I tell Katie about Jamie Fenton? I didn't want her to be upset, but now things are worse!

When Anna arrived at the *Gloss* office on Monday morning, Ruby and Stella were busily planning a fashion shoot. Stella was trying to find a make-up artist, and Ruby was looking for locations – trying to find some good places for the photos.

Anna went to make some coffee, and while she was in the kitchen, she opened the *Gloss* website on her phone and looked at her autumn fashion feature for the hundredth time. She still couldn't believe it when she saw her name. But there was something different about the feature this morning: two comments at the bottom. Anna read them, and her mouth dropped open.

The first comment read:

> **JANE127**
> What a boring feature! There's nothing interesting in this. Gloss's writers are usually good, but this one is terrible!

The one below said:

> **CG2001**
> Who wrote this? Someone who knows nothing
> about fashion! 😄 😄

Ruby came into the kitchen, and looked at Anna's face. 'Are you OK, Anna?' she said.

'Not really,' said Anna. 'Have you seen these comments on my feature?'

'Oh yes, those,' said Ruby. 'Don't worry about them. They're not about you.'

'But they are about me,' said Anna. 'I wrote most of the feature. It's got my name on it!'

Anna felt terrible. Two people thought that her writing was no good. And their comments were underneath her work, online: everyone could see them! She wanted to call Katie, but Katie was not her friend any more. Anna got some coffee cups, and tried not to cry.

'Don't think about it,' said Ruby.

'What will Tina say?' said Anna.

'She won't worry about it,' said Ruby. 'It's just two comments. It's bad luck. If we think that the feature is good, it's good.'

But Anna still felt worried. She was always writing pieces for the school newspaper, and she was usually really happy with them. But in the real world of websites and blogs, perhaps she was not a good writer.

Ruby looked at Anna. 'Listen, I have an idea. I need

words for some photos. You can write a short piece for me if you like.'

'Really?' Anna felt better.

'Yes. But I need it by the end of the day. Three hundred words about being happy.'

Anna laughed. Ruby wanted her to write about being happy, when she felt terrible?

They went to Ruby's desk, and Ruby gave Anna three photos. 'Here you are,' she said. 'I need you to write about the most important things for a happy life. So, we've got holidays, reading *Gloss*, being with your best friend…'

Anna looked down when she heard this.

'What is it?' said Ruby.

'Nothing,' said Anna. 'Just another of my problems right now.' She looked up and smiled at Ruby. 'Thanks for this, Ruby. I'll enjoy writing it.'

A cup of coffee later, Anna was writing at her desk, quickly but carefully. It was noisy in the office again: Stella was talking to a make-up artist on the phone and Ruby was listening to the radio.

How do they do it? Anna thought. She liked to be somewhere nice and quiet when she was writing. When she finished, she read the piece three times before she sent it to Ruby.

This is OK, she thought. It's ready. Those comments were just bad luck.

It was noisy in the office again.

Chapter 6
Tina

Tina did not say anything to Anna about the comments on her feature, but Anna slept badly that night. She could not stop thinking about them. She was tired when she arrived at the office the next day, but she worked really hard all morning. She sent some emails about the fashion shoot for Stella, and posted about it on social media. Then she called some hotels to ask about rooms for the shoot.

At lunchtime, Stella went shopping with Tina to buy some things for the fashion shoot, and Ruby came and sat on Anna's desk.

'Look – I brought lunch today, too!' said Ruby. 'Do you think that Jamie Fenton will come back and ask to eat it with me?'

'Perhaps!' laughed Anna.

'Oh well, even if he doesn't, I need to save money,' said Ruby.

They started to eat, and Anna's phone beeped.

'Ah, that will be your mum,' laughed Ruby. 'Mmm, your lunch looks *so* good.'

'My mum makes it for me,' said Anna. 'I always say that I will do my lunch myself, but she makes it before I wake up in the morning.'

'That's nice,' said Ruby.

'Hmm,' said Anna. 'My mum's great, but sometimes she forgets that I'm fifteen now!'

'But does she like you working here?'

Anna laughed. 'My mum is happy for me because she knows that I want to write, but she doesn't understand websites. She thinks that teenagers spend too much time online and need to talk more.'

Ruby laughed. 'Perhaps she's right.'

The office door opened, and Tina walked in. Stella was behind her, looking worried.

Ruby stopped eating. 'Tina, would you like to see our ideas for the shoot? We—'

But Tina didn't wait to hear about Ruby's ideas.

'Look!' she said, and she put her tablet on Anna's desk. 'Have you seen this?'

The *Gloss* website was open on Tina's tablet, and when Anna and Ruby looked, they saw Anna's piece about being happy, and the photos.

There were some comments underneath, and when Anna started to read them, a horrible feeling came into her stomach.

CG2001

This is so boring – and the writing is terrible. The features in Teen Talks are better than this.

Ruby looked up at Tina. 'That's not true,' she said. 'This is a good piece.'

There were other comments, too. Anna did not really want to read them, but she looked at them quickly. None of them were good. Another one said:

> **JANE127**
> Anna Hall knows nothing about being happy. What is she talking about?

There were other comments, too.

Tina said, 'Ruby, what's all this about? Why did Anna write this? Usually you do the words for small pieces like this.'

'Sorry, Tina,' said Ruby. 'But I knew that Anna wanted to do this, and she writes well. She really does. She did a good job. I don't understand these comments. People are so unkind online sometimes.'

Anna looked at Tina.

'This is very difficult,' said Tina. 'Anna, I usually only let interns make the coffee and help a little. Writing for the website is a big thing.'

'I know,' replied Anna. Her voice was shaking.

'I know that you're a good writer at your school,' Tina said. 'But it's not working very well here on a real website. Because *Gloss* is new, we really can't have comments like this. I didn't say anything about the comments on the fashion feature yesterday, but I have to do something about this now.'

Anna looked at the floor. Tina was right: she was just a schoolgirl who liked writing stories. She was stupid to try and write features for *Gloss*.

'I'm going to my office,' said Tina.

She walked away, and Ruby and Stella both looked at Anna, worried.

'I'll be in the fashion room,' said Anna quietly.

Chapter 7
Answers

Anna sat in the dark in the fashion room, crying. Perhaps I'll just stay in here, she thought. I lost my best friend for nothing. I'll never be a writer. And now Tina is going to ask me to leave *Gloss*, I just know it.

How did this happen? It was strange because her piece did not look very different from the others on the website. But people really hated it.

Anna opened the website on her phone and looked at the new comments.

> **CG2001**
> Great photos, but really boring writing.
>
> **JANE127**
> Why is an intern writing features?

Anna started reading the next comment, but then suddenly stopped, and looked back at the last one again. Wait a minute… The piece had her name at the top, but that was all. It did not say anywhere on the website that she was an intern!

Anna looked at the name above the comment: 'JANE127'. I don't know anyone called Jane, Anna thought. But then suddenly she remembered something: Jane was Katie's middle name, and 127 was her house number.

Anna looked at the first comment again, which said that the writing was boring. The name above the comment was 'CG2001'.

Carla Giles! Anna thought.

She looked back at the comments on her first feature about autumn fashion. The comments had the same names on them: 'JANE127' and 'CG2001'!

Anna read all the other comments. She did not know the names. Are these real comments, thought Anna, or did Katie ask people to write them? Does everyone hate me?

The door of the fashion room opened, and Stella looked in.

'Anna, do we have a red hat for the... Anna, why are you sitting in the dark? Are you OK?'

Stella turned on the light and came inside.

Anna looked away. She did not want Stella to know that she was crying. But to Anna's surprise, Stella came and sat next to her on the floor.

'Don't worry about those comments,' said Stella. 'People say stupid things sometimes.'

'Tina's going to ask me to leave early, I know it,' said Anna. 'She's going to find someone better.'

'No, she isn't,' said Stella.

'It's not just that,' said Anna. 'I think that my friends left those comments!'

'I think that my friends left those comments!'

'Really?' said Stella, and she took Anna's phone from the floor and looked at it silently.

'I think that they told everyone at school to write

comments, too,' said Anna.

'That's terrible, Anna,' said Stella. 'You need to talk to your teachers about this. And you must tell Tina.'

'Oh no!' said Anna. 'I don't want Tina to know about it. She didn't really want me to write for *Gloss*, and if she knows about this, she'll never have an intern here again!'

'That's not true,' said Stella. 'A few bad comments aren't the end of the world for *Gloss*. But this is horrible for you, and we need to do something. Why don't you speak to your mum? Perhaps she can phone the school?'

Anna did not want her mum to phone the school, but she knew that Stella was right.

'OK,' she said. 'I'll talk to my mum tonight. Thanks.'

'Good,' said Stella, getting up. 'Now come and have a cup of coffee.'

'I'll just wait here for a minute or two,' said Anna. 'My face looks terrible.'

'Ah, I know what you need!' laughed Stella. She went to the make-up cupboard, and looked for something. 'There, now put some of this on.' She gave Anna some make-up. 'It hides everything!'

Anna put some on. She still had red eyes, but she felt better.

'Thanks,' she said.

'Keep it,' said Stella.

* * *

When Anna got off the train after work that day, she felt really tired. She knew that Stella was right, and that she needed to tell her mum about the comments. But she did not want her mum to phone the school. Will anyone ever speak to me again after that? she thought.

She started to walk down the street, but then she felt a hand on her arm.

It was Katie!

'I need to speak to you, Anna,' said Katie. 'I've done something terrible.'

'The comments, you mean?' said Anna. 'I know that it was you already. Why did you do that?'

'I'm so sorry, Anna,' said Katie. 'I thought that it was funny at first, but now I feel terrible.'

'And you told people from school to write comments, too!' said Anna.

Katie looked surprised. 'No,' she said. 'We didn't talk to anyone from school.'

'But there were lots of comments!' said Anna.

Katie put her hands over her mouth. 'Oh no!' she said. 'She didn't do it, did she?' She looked at Anna, and started to explain. 'I was at Carla's house when we made the comments this morning. Carla wanted to leave more, and use lots of different names. She thought that it was funny. I said that it was too much and I went home. I didn't think that she would do it.'

Anna did not say anything.

'*I need to speak to you, Anna. I've done something terrible.*'

'I'm really sorry, Anna,' said Katie. 'I was upset because you didn't say anything about meeting Jamie Fenton. And,' she looked down, 'I was jealous, too. Really jealous. You have a great job this summer, and I'm working at Scarf Shop! But your writing is really good. You were the right person for the job. I see that now.'

Anna smiled. 'Well, the Editor doesn't think that,' she said. 'I don't think she wants me to write any more pieces for *Gloss*.'

'Oh, Anna!' said Katie. 'Can't you tell her? Explain that it was your friends. Say that we were being stupid.'

'You don't know Tina,' said Anna. 'You can't really talk to her about that kind of thing. And because *Gloss* is so new, she's really worried about any bad comments.'

Katie was silent, then she said, 'I'm really sorry, Anna. I know that I've done a terrible thing, but… can we be friends again? I like talking to you every day. I miss that.'

Anna looked at Katie. 'I do too,' she said, and smiled. 'I was stupid. I didn't know how to tell you about the job, or about Jamie Fenton. So I just didn't.'

'I can understand that now,' said Katie. 'And I've been a terrible friend. Look, why don't you come to my house for dinner?'

'I'd like that,' said Anna. 'I'll call my mum. She'll be happy when she hears that we're friends again.'

The girls started to walk down Katie's street. 'Right,' said Katie, 'now I want to hear all about Jamie Fenton!'

Chapter 8
An Idea

OK, thought Anna, when she arrived at the *Gloss* office the next morning, things are not good at *Gloss* – but Katie and I are friends again... and that's more important.

She got the mail as usual and walked to Tina's office, but before she could knock, Tina opened the door.

'Anna,' said Tina, 'do you have five minutes?'

Anna went into Tina's office, and sat down nervously. Tina is going to ask me to leave early, she thought. I know it! Perhaps there are jobs at Scarf Shop... I'll ask Katie.

'I had a phone call from your friend Katie this morning,' said Tina.

Anna looked at Tina, surprised.

'She told me what happened,' said Tina. 'Why didn't you say that those comments were made by your friends?'

'I didn't know at first,' said Anna. 'And when I found out, I thought that you would be angry. I know that comments like that are not good for *Gloss*.'

'Look at this, Anna,' said Tina, and she moved her laptop across the desk. The website was open at Anna's feature about autumn fashion, and at the bottom, underneath the comments from Carla and Katie, there were some new ones:

CLARE101
I think that this writer is great. What is JANE127 talking about?

ELJ200
Really enjoyed this feature. Some great ideas – and very funny and interesting!

There were more, and they all said good things. Tina looked at Anna. 'They're right,' she said. 'When I saw the bad comments, I just thought, why did I say that an intern could write a feature? But look – these are real comments, and these people like your work.'

Anna smiled. 'Thanks, Tina.'

'Of course, after all this, perhaps you don't want to write any more features while you're here!'

'Oh, I do!' said Anna.

'Good,' said Tina. 'Well, Stella is starting a feature about eye make-up tomorrow. Perhaps you can help her.'

'That's great,' said Anna. Then she said nervously, 'I have another idea for a feature. I'd really like to write about what's happened: about people making horrible comments online. Can I do that today?'

'That's a good idea,' said Tina. 'OK. Show me when you've finished.'

'Thank you, Tina.' Anna was smiling when she went back to her desk. She took her laptop from her bag, and walked across the office.

'Where are you going?' asked Ruby.

'To the fashion room,' answered Anna. 'I like it in there. It's nice and quiet. I'm only coming out when I've written a new feature, a really good one!'

'These are real comments, and these people like your work.'

Chapter 9
Home Page

Two days later, Anna was working on Stella's eye make-up feature before lunch.

'Your mum hasn't sent you any messages today!' said Ruby.

'No,' laughed Anna. 'She read my feature yesterday. I think that at last she knows that I'm not a little girl!'

Anna opened the *Gloss* website and looked happily at her feature for the tenth time. It was on the *Gloss* home page!

Comments that hurt!
Anna Hall

When I started writing for *Gloss*, I thought excitedly about everybody who reads the features on this website. But I never thought about horrible comments. And when I got some, it really hurt! Some people from my school were posting the comments, and when I found that out, it felt even worse. I thought that everyone hated me!

I know that I am not alone. Trolling – writing bad things online – is a big problem. Four out of ten teenagers say that someone has been horrible to them online.

'It's easy to write unkind things online,' says Dr Sandra Berger, who helps teenagers with problems. 'People forget that a real person will read their comments. It is important to think carefully before you write something.'

So what have I learned from this? Do not use social media or websites to tell someone that you are angry with them. Sometimes it is better to talk. Perhaps it is more difficult at first, but when we are face to face, we can say sorry, explain things, and understand why another person is angry.

What do you think? Post your comments!

'How many comments do you have now?' asked Stella.

Anna looked at the bottom of the page. 'Oh! Thirty-one now!' she said.

She looked at the latest one. It said:

YANNI_F
Yes! This is so true! Why are people horrible online? Do they think that no one can see them? They're wrong: thousands of people can!

'Anna, there's someone here to see you,' said Stella.

'Perhaps it's Jamie Fenton!' cried Ruby. She got out her lunch and said, 'I'm here, Jamie! I've got cookies!'

Anna laughed. She looked up and saw Katie standing at the door.

'Are you ready for lunch?' Katie asked Anna.

'Yes!' said Anna. 'Come in for a minute.'

Katie came inside the office. 'This is great, Anna,' she said, looking around. 'You look at home here!'

Anna smiled.

'Are you going out for lunch today, Anna?' said Ruby.

'Yes! You don't get a feature on the *Gloss* home page every day!' said Anna.

'Oh, I bought you something,' said Katie. She gave Anna a Scarf Shop bag.

'It's not my birthday,' said Anna.

'I know,' said Katie. 'Have a look.'

Anna opened the bag. Inside, there was a really nice scarf with little pencils on it.

'Because you're a writer,' explained Katie.

'I love it!' said Anna. 'Oh – wait a minute.' She ran into the fashion room, then came out. She gave Katie a small white box. 'And this is for you,' she said. 'Ruby and Stella said that it was OK.'

Katie opened the box. 'Ooh, make-up. And a picture of Jamie Fenton! Thank you!' She looked really happy. She said, 'If he comes into the office again, tell me immediately!'

'And me!' called Ruby from her desk.

'Ooh, make-up. And a picture of Jamie Fenton!'

Anna laughed. She walked to the office door with Katie.

'Don't be too long,' said Ruby. 'It's the ideas meeting this afternoon. Tina wants you to be there!'

'OK,' said Anna, smiling. She looked around at the busy, noisy office. Suddenly she felt really happy. At last, she belonged. It was nearly the end of the summer, but she had a plan for the next year: to write as much as possible. If I work hard, she thought, then I can do… well, anything!

GLOSSARY

beauty *(n)*   being beautiful

beep *(v)*   to make a short high noise

believe *(v)*   to feel sure that something is true

blog *(n)*   a page on a website that a person or group of people write onto regularly, e.g. every day or every few days, with news about something

comment *(n)*   something that you say or write; it shows what you think about something

cookie *(n)*   something sweet to eat

Editor *(n)*   the person who decides what to put in a newspaper, website, or magazine

fashion *(n)*   a way of dressing or wearing your hair that lots of people like for a time

feature *(n)*   a piece of writing in a newspaper/magazine, or on a website, about something or somebody

hate *(v)*   to feel very strongly that you do not like somebody or something

hit *(n)*   when someone visits a page on a website

home page *(n)*   the first page on a website

horrible *(adj)*   very bad; not nice

idea *(n)*   a plan, or something that you think of

intern *(n)*   a student or young person who does a job (often unpaid) to learn about it; **internship** *(n)*   a time of being an intern

interview *(v & n)*   to meet somebody (often famous) to ask them questions for e.g. a newspaper or website

jealous *(adj)*   angry or sad because you want what another person has

laptop *(n)*   a small computer that is easy to carry

mail *(n)* letters and parcels that people send

make-up *(n)* things like lipstick or powder that you put on your eyes, face, or mouth to change how you look

make-up artist *(n)* someone who puts make-up on people for their job

message *(v & n)* to send words to someone by phone or through a computer

miss *(v)* to feel sad about somebody or something that has gone

nervous *(adj)* worried or afraid

online *(adj)* using the Internet

parcel *(n)* something bigger than a letter that you send to somebody, wrapped in paper

piece *(n)* some writing in a newspaper or magazine, or on a website

post *(v)* (in this story) to put a comment or piece on a website or blog

problem *(n)* something that is difficult; something that you worry about

scarf *(n)* something that you wear around your neck or head to keep you warm, or for fashion (plural **scarves**)

shoot *(n)* (in this story) a time that is planned for someone to make a film, or to take photos for a book, magazine, or website

social media *(n)* programs on computers and phones that people use to talk to and show things to other people

tablet *(n)* a very small, flat computer that you can carry with you

teenager *(n)* a person who is between thirteen and nineteen years old

upset *(adj)* feeling unhappy or worried

vlog *(n)* a video blog

The Summer Intern

ACTIVITIES

ACTIVITIES

Before Reading

1 **Choose the correct words to complete these definitions.**

1 a laptop: a *computer / table* that you can carry with you

2 a home page: the first page *in a book / on a website*

3 a problem: something that is *difficult / exciting*

4 jealous: angry or sad because you *want what another person has / don't like what another person does*

5 mail: *letters and parcels / bags and suitcases*

6 online: using *a computer / the Internet*

2 **Look at the title, front cover, and back cover. Match each name with the correct description.**

1 *Gloss*   a Anna's best friend

2 Anna   b *Gloss*'s Editor

3 Tina   c a summer intern

4 Katie   d a fashion and beauty website

3 **What do you think will happen in the story? Write *Yes* or *No*.**

1 Anna and Katie will make friends again.

2 The Editor will ask Anna to stay at *Gloss* after the summer.

3 Anna's mother will stop phoning her every day.

4 Anna will leave *Gloss* and find another summer job.

ACTIVITIES

While Reading

Read Chapter 1. Then write the names of the characters.

1 _____ is *Gloss*'s Fashion and Beauty Writer.
2 _____ is the *Gloss* Photographer.
3 _____ wants to write something about social media.
4 _____ does not like anyone's ideas.
5 _____ is in the group High Five.

Which sentence best describes how Anna is feeling about *Gloss*?

1 She doesn't like the Editor and wants a job in a shop.
2 She is excited to be there, and happy to listen and learn.
3 She likes working there, but wants to do some more interesting things.
4 She wants to be a writer, but she thinks that a teenagers' website is the wrong place for her.

Read Chapter 2. Complete the sentences with *Anna*, *Katie*, or *Anna and Katie*.

1 _____ love(s) books and writing.
2 _____ love(s) beauty and fashion.
3 _____ wanted the internship at *Gloss*.
4 _____ got a job at Scarf Shop.
5 _____ started sitting next to Carla.

Read Chapter 3. Put the events in order.

a Jamie Fenton arrives in the office.

b Anna phones Tina.

c Ruby goes out for lunch with Stella.

d Anna's mum sends her a text.

e Anna's mum arrives in the office.

Complete the questions with *wh* words, and answer them.

1 _____ tidies the fashion room?

2 _____ are Ruby and Stella not there when
   Jamie arrives?

3 _____ do Anna and Jamie talk about?

4 _____ is Tina when Anna phones her?

Read Chapter 4. Are the sentences true or false?

1 Tina is pleased with the Jamie Fenton interview.

2 Anna has an exciting day at *Gloss*.

3 Katie likes her job at Scarf Shop.

4 Anna forgets to tell Katie about Jamie Fenton.

Read Chapter 5. Tick the two sentences that are true.

1 Anna thinks that her friends wrote the comments on
   the website.

2 Ruby wants Anna to feel better.

3 Anna thinks that it is easy to work in the *Gloss* office.

4 Anna is pleased with her piece about being happy.

Read Chapter 6. Write *Ruby* or *Tina*.

1 _____ has lunch with Anna.
2 _____ is angry that Anna wrote the piece about being happy.
3 _____ thinks that Anna's piece is good.
4 _____ does not want Anna to write for *Gloss*.

Complete the sentences with the correct word.

emails   feature   online   tablet   website

1 In the morning, Anna sends some _____ about the fashion shoot.
2 Anna's mum thinks that teenagers spend too much time _____.
3 Tina shows Anna and Ruby the comments on her _____.
4 Tina saw the comments on Anna's fashion _____, too.
5 Tina is worried because the _____ is new.

Read Chapter 7. Who...

1 wants Anna to talk to her mum?
2 is afraid that she will lose all her friends?
3 wrote most of the comments under Anna's piece?
4 knows that she has not been a good friend?

Choose the correct words to complete the sentences.

1 Anna thinks that JANE127 is *Carla / Katie*.
2 Anna doesn't want to tell *Tina / Stella* who wrote the comments.
3 Katie wants to hear about *Stella / Jamie Fenton*.

Read Chapter 8. Put the events in order.

a Tina asks Anna to go into her office.
b Anna takes her laptop into the fashion room.
c Anna reads some good comments about her feature.
d Katie phones Tina.
e Anna has an idea for another feature.

Read Chapter 9. Tick the thing Anna says in her feature.

1 She was surprised when people posted horrible comments about her pieces.
2 Most teenagers have had horrible comments online.
3 She says: never use social media.
4 It is always easy to say sorry face to face.

What happens in Chapter 9? Write *Yes* or *No*.

1 Anna gets some more horrible comments.
2 Katie gives Anna a special scarf.
3 Ruby meets Jamie Fenton.
4 Anna and Katie go out for lunch.

ACTIVITIES

After Reading

Vocabulary

1 Complete the paragraph with the words below.

blog   comments   Editor   fashion   horrible   online

When the ¹_____ asked me to write a ²_____
about ³_____, I was very excited. After the first day,
there were lots of ⁴_____. Most of them were really
nice, but two were ⁵_____. At first, I didn't want to
write any more, but one of the feature writers told me not to
worry. 'People say stupid things ⁶_____,' she said.

**2 How does Anna feel in each situation below? Unscramble
the words to find the correct adjective.**

steup   sujaleo   vunoser

1 Tina has asked Anna's friend Katie to write a new blog
for *Gloss* – but Anna wanted to write the blog herself.

2 She is going to a party with Tina, and won't know
anyone there.

3 Katie has sent her a text which says, 'I don't want to be
your friend any more.'

Grammar

1 **Complete the sentences in the past continuous. Use the words in brackets.**

We _____ (get) lots of hits, but we needed more.
We were getting lots of hits, but we needed more.

1 Anna _____ (look for) her lunch when Jamie Fenton came into the office.

2 Anna _____ (think) about her day when she got off the train.

3 Katie _____ (walk) in front of Anna.

4 In the office, Stella _____ (talk) on the phone and Ruby _____ (listen) to the radio.

5 Katie _____ (smile) when she arrived.

6 People from Anna's school _____ (post) the horrible comments on the website.

2 **Write sentences with a *that* clause, using the words below.**

forget ~~hear~~ *know remember think*

Katie: Anna has got the job at *Gloss*.
Katie hears that Anna has got the job at Gloss.

1 Anna's mum: Teenagers spend too much time online.

2 Tina: Her interview with Jamie Fenton is on Friday.

3 Anna's mum: Anna is fifteen years old.

4 Anna: Jane is Katie's middle name.

Reading

1 **Which character is thinking these things, and what has just happened when they are thinking them?**

1 That poor girl! Why did her friends write those things? I really want her to call her mum. I haven't talked to her much before, but she's a nice girl.

2 I must get back to the office quickly. I know that he won't wait for long.

3 She said that we would have no more secrets, so why didn't she tell me about this? OK, I'm jealous – but I'm also really upset!

4 She had a good idea – I feel sorry for her. Why was Tina so unkind? Is she worrying about the interview?

2 **Put the sentences in the correct order.**

a Anna and Katie meet, and talk about their jobs, and Anna says that she will come to Katie's house one evening.

b Katie sees the photo of Anna with Jamie Fenton and is upset.

c Anna writes a piece about being happy.

d Jamie Fenton comes to the *Gloss* office.

e Katie starts to sit next to Carla in all their lessons.

f Katie says sorry for her horrible comments.

Writing

1 Read the comments about a feature on a website. Was the title *You are what you wear* or *Fashion doesn't matter*?

Catgirl596
Yes, this is so true! I go to lots of markets and special shops to find cheap but unusual clothes, because I think that this shows people who I am.

Jake99
I don't think that you can look at someone's clothes and see what kind of person they are. I don't spend a lot of time or money on clothes because they aren't important to me, so I'm always wearing boring old things. But I'm not old and boring!

2 Complete the chart with ticks or crosses.

Who...?	Catgirl596	Jake99	You
agrees with the statement in the title of the feature	☐	☐	☐
thinks a lot about clothes	☐	☐	☐
spends a lot of money on clothes	☐	☐	☐

3 Write a comment to reply to Catgirl596 or Jake99. Do you agree/disagree with them? Why? What do you think about fashion, and the statement in the title?

Speaking

1 Read the conversations. What do the words in bold refer to?

KATIE: I was upset because I didn't want to hear **something like that** from Carla.

ANNA: I'm really sorry. I didn't know how to tell you.

KATIE: Well, next time, tell me first, OK? Do you want to come to my house one evening this week?

KATIE: I need to speak to you. I've done **something terrible**.

ANNA: I know that it was you. Why did you do that?

KATIE: I was upset because you didn't say anything about meeting Jamie Fenton. I was jealous, too. I know that I've done a terrible thing, but… can we be friends again?

2 Underline the phrases below in exercise 1.

1 I've done something terrible.
   I know that I've done a terrible thing.
   I'm really sorry.

2 I was upset because…
   I was jealous.
   I didn't know how to tell you.

3 Can we be friends again?
   Do you want to (come to my house)…?

3 Match each group of phrases from exercise 2 with the reason for saying them below.

   a To explain your reasons for doing/saying something.
   b To say sorry, or to say that you have done something wrong.
   c To try to make friends again.

4 In pairs, role-play two conversations. Imagine that you are two people who are making friends after an argument about the things below. Use the phrases in exercise 2.

   • One friend writes a horrible comment about the other on social media.
   • One friend goes home early from the other's party.

5 Discuss the questions with a partner. Use the words below to help you.

I really enjoyed…   the bit when…
I think the story was…   I didn't like…   the scene when…

   1 Which scenes in the story did you enjoy the most?
   2 What bits of the story did you not like?
   3 Who was your favourite character, and were there any characters who you did not like? Why?
   4 What is your opinion of *The Summer Intern*?

THE OXFORD BOOKWORMS LIBRARY

THE OXFORD BOOKWORMS LIBRARY is a best-selling series of graded readers which provides authentic and enjoyable reading in English. It includes a wide range of original and adapted texts: classic and modern fiction, non-fiction, and plays. There are more than 250 Bookworms to choose from, in seven carefully graded language stages that go from beginner to advanced level.

Each Bookworm is illustrated, and offers extensive support, including:

- ▸ a glossary of above-level words
- ▸ activities to develop language and communication skills
- ▸ notes about the author and story
- ▸ online tests

Each Bookworm pack contains a reader and audio.

6	STAGE 6	▸ 2500 HEADWORDS	▸ CEFR B2–C1
5	STAGE 5	▸ 1800 HEADWORDS	▸ CEFR B2
4	STAGE 4	▸ 1400 HEADWORDS	▸ CEFR B1–B2
3	STAGE 3	▸ 1000 HEADWORDS	▸ CEFR B1
2	STAGE 2	▸ 700 HEADWORDS	▸ CEFR A2–B1
1	STAGE 1	▸ 400 HEADWORDS	▸ CEFR A1–A2
S	STARTER	▸ 250 HEADWORDS	▸ CEFR A1

Find a full list of *Bookworms* and resources at
www.oup.com/elt/gradedreaders

If you liked this Bookworm, why not try...

Matty Doolin
CATHERINE COOKSON

Matty is fifteen and about to leave school. He wants to work on a farm, but his parents say he is too young to leave home. They also say that his dog, Nelson, has to go. But it is because of Nelson that Matty finds a new life...